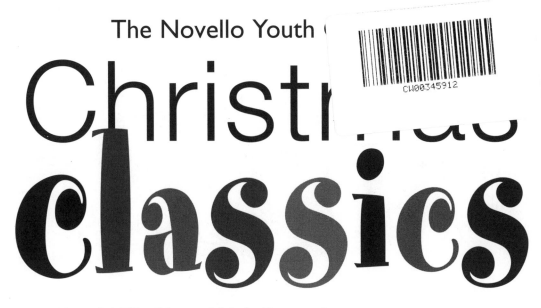

The Novello Youth Chorals
Christmas classics

For SATB Choir With Piano Accompaniment

Published by:
Novello Publishing Limited
8/9 Frith Street, London, W1D 3JB, England.

Exclusive distributors:
Music Sales Limited
Distribution Centre, Newmarket Road, Bury St Edmunds, Suffolk, IP33 3YB.

Music Sales Pty Limited
120 Rothschild Avenue, Rosebery, NSW 2018, Australia.

Order No. NOV170588
ISBN 1-84449-598-1
This collection © Copyright 2004 Novello & Company Limited.

Arranged by Berty Rice.
Music processed by Note-orious Productions Limited.
Compiled by Nick Crispin.
Printed in the United Kingdom.

www.musicsales.com

Novello Publishing Limited
part of The Music Sales Group
London / New York / Paris / Sydney / Copenhagen / Berlin / Madrid / Tokyo

Blue Christmas

Words & Music by Billy Hayes & Jay Johnson

3

4

Here Comes Santa Claus

Words & Music by Gene Autry & Oakley Haldeman

11

Jump in bed 'n' co - ver up your head 'cos San-ta Claus comes to-night.

Jump in bed 'n' co - ver up your head 'cos San-ta Claus comes to-night.

Jump in bed 'n' co - ver up your head 'cos San-ta Claus comes to-night.

Jump in bed 'n' co - ver up your head 'cos San-ta Claus comes to-night.

Let's give thanks to the Lord a - bove 'cos San-ta Claus comes to -

Let's give thanks to the Lord a - bove 'cos San-ta Claus comes to -

Let's give thanks to the Lord a - bove 'cos San-ta Claus comes to -

Let's give thanks to the Lord a - bove 'cos San-ta Claus comes to -

15

Jingle Bell Rock

Words & Music by Joseph Beal & James Boothe

21

⊕ **CODA**

that's the jin-gle bell, that's the jin-gle bell rock.

that's the jin-gle bell, that's the jin-gle bell rock.

that's the jin-gle bell, that's the jin-gle bell rock.

that's the jin-gle bell, that's the jin-gle bell rock.

Let It Snow! Let It Snow! Let It Snow!

Words by Sammy Cahn
Music by Jule Styne

25

I Saw Mommy Kissing Santa Claus

Words & Music by Tommie Connor